Finger Plays
for Home and School

Jeanne Cheyney
Arnold Cheyney

Scott, Foresman and Company
Glenview, Illinois   London

®Good Year Books

are available for preschool through grade 12 and
for every basic curriculum subject plus many
enrichment areas. For more Good Year Books,
contact your local bookseller or educational dealer.
For a complete catalog with information about
other Good Year Books, please write:

Good Year Books
Department GYB
1900 East Lake Avenue
Glenview, Illinois 60025

Introduction

All the poems in FINGER PLAYS FOR HOME AND SCHOOL are original. They touch upon home, school, holidays, seasons, and other areas that children experience. They promote language development and mathematical concepts, foster auditory discrimination, and utilize the motoric capabilities and innate rhythm of children.

Each page in the book contains a poem with finger movements and suggested activities for extending the finger play either before or after introducing the poem. Two pages of finger puppets are included. All the pages may be duplicated for home and classroom use.

Parents and teachers: If desired, add puppets to your fingers (see pp. 43 and 44) and use the same finger movements from each page of FINGER PLAYS FOR HOME AND SCHOOL or create new movements. Then, encourage children to use the puppets in the same way.

About The Authors

Jeanne Cheyney studied at the Cleveland School of Art and graduated from Kent State University in Art Education. She taught in grades two through four. She writes and illustrates for educational book and magazine publishers. In the trade-book area, she has published one young-adult novel and three historical romances.

Arnold Cheyney is a professor of education at the University of Miami in Coral Gables, Florida, where he teaches language arts and children's literature. He and his wife, Jeanne, have collaborated on numerous books and articles over the years. This is their eighth Good Year Book.

Table of Contents

Today is my birthday

Today is my birthday.
I'll have a fine cake
As high as the sky and
As big as a lake.

With frosting so thick
You can ski on the top
And slide down the side,
Without having to stop!

I'll have candles as big
As large telephone poles.
When I pull them all out,
They'll make deep and wide holes.

You'll each have a fork
And a big silver spoon.
You'll have a huge plate
As large as the moon.

You can eat all you want
Of my lovely white cake,
But you eat it all gone and
Your stomach will ache!

Activities: What special things
do you do on your birthday?
Write or tell a story about the kind
of birthday party you would like to
have. Draw a picture of your
birthday party.

I reach up for my toothbrush

I reach up for my toothbrush
And I hold the tube of paste.
With care, I twist the tiny cap,
Go slowly, without haste.

I gently squeeze the tube,
Then put a little on my brush.
Adding water to it all,
I am careful not to rush.

I tip the bristles upward,
Bring them down my upper teeth.
Then I tip the bristles down and
Brush them up my lower teeth.

I rinse my mouth with water and
My teeth look bright and clean.
If I take my time to brush them,
They're the nicest ever seen!

Activities: Read about teeth. Draw pictures of foods that help your teeth stay healthy. Tell or write about a trip to the dentist.

What can fingers find to do?

What can fingers find to do?
Wash the dishes,
Sweep the floor.
Climb a ladder,
Close the door.

Pick some flowers,
Wash my hair.
Hold a book
And move a chair.

What can fingers find to do?
Feed the kitten,
Hold a tray.
Pick up toys
And fold to pray.

Set the table,
Make a pie.
Iron a shirt
And wave good-bye.

Activities: What other good things can fingers do? Do fingers ever do unkind things? When? What activities make fingers dirty? Clean?

3

I sort the dirty clothes

I sort the dirty clothes
Into piles of dark and light.
I measure soap into a cup
And turn the dial right.

Wash-water comes a-pouring in,
Filling to the top.
I dump my cup of soap right in.
The bubbles heap and pop.

The agitator twists and turns.
I put my white clothes in.
Swish and swirl, swish and swirl,
The washer starts to spin.

When it stops, the clothes are clean,
Looking nice and bright.
I hang them on the line to dry,
While clothespins hold them tight.

When all the clothes blow nice and dry,
I take them from the line.
I fold them very carefully.
They smell so fresh and fine.

Activities: How do your mother or father do the laundry? Act out the finger-play poem while a friend reads it. Draw pictures of the poem to put in sequence. If you didn't have a washing machine, how would you wash your clothes?

SOAP

With both of my hands

With both of my hands,
I take a small cup.
I open the popcorn
And fill my cup up.

I get out the popper
And put the corn in.
I plug in the popper
And watch the fan spin.

I soon hear a Pop! Pop!
Then Pop! Pop! and Pop!
I find a big pan—
Kernels heap to the top.

I add melted butter,
Put salt on the top.
I love to eat popcorn.
I'll just never stop!

Activities: Pretend you are kernels popping and act out what you would do. Make rabbits or cats and glue on popcorn for fur. Watch corn pop and tell why you think the kernels burst open.

From *Finger Plays for Home and School*, Copyright © 1990 Scott, Foresman and Company.

5

I reach up for my cloth and soap

I reach up for my cloth and soap,
Then climb into the tub.
I pull the shower curtain shut,
Add water, start to rub.

My cloth is nice and soapy
As I scrub my neck and arm.
I wash myself all over, for,
The water's good and warm.

I reach up for shampoo and
Put a little in my hand.
I wash my hair and rinse, and
Oh, I feel so clean and grand!

Activities: Tell about the ways you
keep clean. Read about germs. Look
at germs through a microscope.

The big yellow bus

The big yellow bus
Rolls along down the street.
Then the horn toots at me
And I jump to my feet.

Squeak, squeak, go the brakes
And the door opens wide.
Then I hop up the steps
And I hurry inside.

By the window I sit
For the air is so cool.
There I ride on the bus
All the way to my school.

Activities: Why do schools need buses? What kinds of rules do you need on buses? Draw pictures of children going to school on the school bus.

ABC

ABC
Look at me!

DEF
I see Jeff.

GHI
Catch a fly.

JKL
Ring a bell.

MNO
See my toe.

PQR
Drive a car.

STU
Tap my shoe.

VWX
One bird pecks.

Then, YZ
Smart, like me.

Activities: Look for alphabet letters in the room. Cut alphabet letters from magazines and newspapers. Glue upper-case and lowercase letters on paper.

A is for animals

A is for animals, both big and small.

B is for bear, that grows very tall.

C is for cat, curling up in my lap.

D is for dog. See him taking a nap?

E is for elephant, so big and so gray.

F is for father, who asks me to play.

G is for gum. Here, I'll share it with you.

H is for helping, which I like to do.

I is for icing, to spread on our cake.

J is for jungle, with lots of big snakes.

K is for kitten, so soft and so small.

L is for love, which I have for you all.

M is for mother, who takes care of me.

N is for nice, which we always should be.

O is for oak, the name of a tree.

P is for popper, that pops corn for me.

Q is for quiet, a good word to know.

R is for rain, helping gardens to grow.

S is for sun, that warms all the land.

T is for turtle, laying eggs in the sand.

U is for up, where I go on my swing.

V is for violets that grow in the spring.

W is for wings, that you see on a bee.

X is for x-ray, to look inside me.

Y is for yellow, a color so bright.

Z is for zebra, with stripes black as night.

Activities: With your finger, write the alphabet letters on the wall. Write the alphabet letters on paper. Think of other words that begin with the letters of the alphabet.

From *Finger Plays for Home and School*, Copyright © 1990 Scott, Foresman and Company.

A - ape

A - ape
B - ball
C - cat
D - doll.

E - eat
F - flat
G - goat
H - hat.

I - iron
J - jump
K - kitchen
L - lump.

M - mop
N - nose
O - open
P - pose.

Q - quiet
R - rap
S - see
T - tap.

U - up
V - vibraphone
W - watch
X - xylophone.

Y - yes
Z - zoo
And now can you
All say them, too?

Activities: Draw each letter in the air as you say the poem. Form your body into each alphabet letter. March to the beat of the poem as you say it.

5 little apples

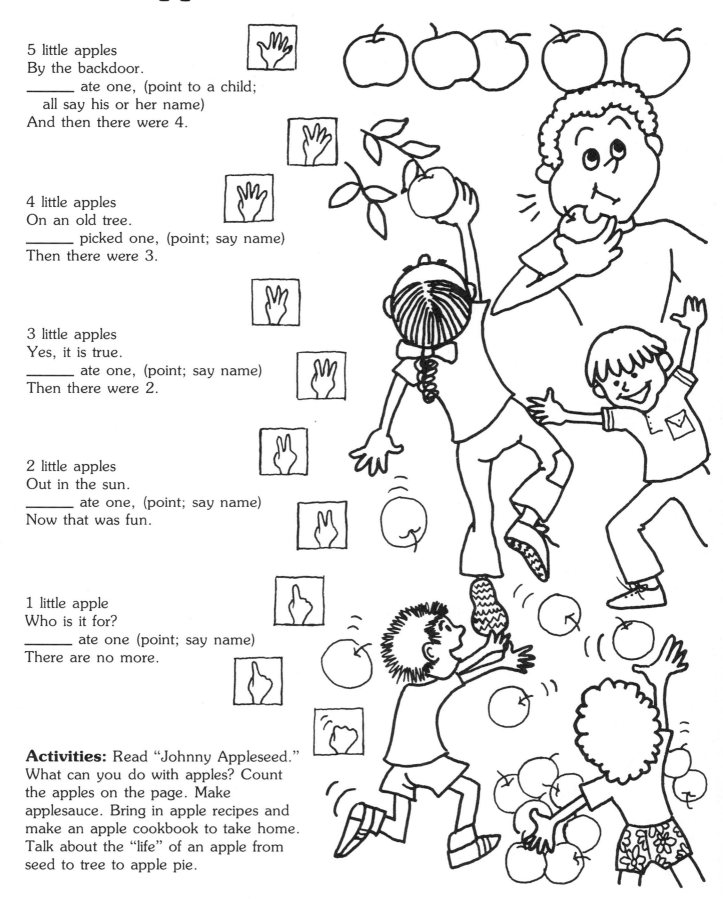

5 little apples
By the backdoor.
_____ ate one, (point to a child;
  all say his or her name)
And then there were 4.

4 little apples
On an old tree.
_____ picked one, (point; say name)
Then there were 3.

3 little apples
Yes, it is true.
_____ ate one, (point; say name)
Then there were 2.

2 little apples
Out in the sun.
_____ ate one, (point; say name)
Now that was fun.

1 little apple
Who is it for?
_____ ate one (point; say name)
There are no more.

Activities: Read "Johnny Appleseed."
What can you do with apples? Count
the apples on the page. Make
applesauce. Bring in apple recipes and
make an apple cookbook to take home.
Talk about the "life" of an apple from
seed to tree to apple pie.

A little fly walked <u>on</u> my chin

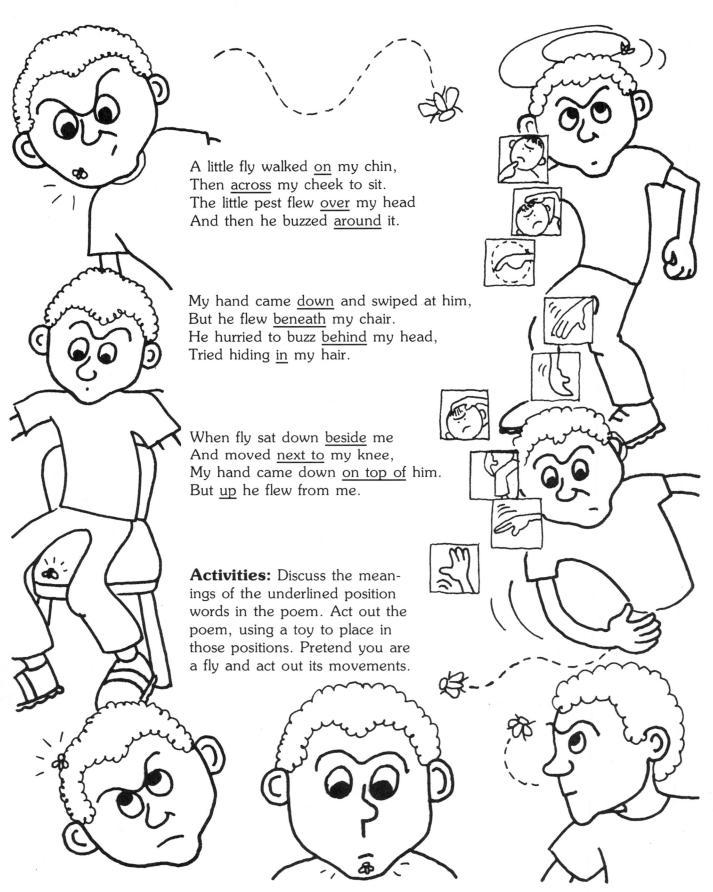

A little fly walked <u>on</u> my chin,
Then <u>across</u> my cheek to sit.
The little pest flew <u>over</u> my head
And then he buzzed <u>around</u> it.

My hand came <u>down</u> and swiped at him,
But he flew <u>beneath</u> my chair.
He hurried to buzz <u>behind</u> my head,
Tried hiding <u>in</u> my hair.

When fly sat down <u>beside</u> me
And moved <u>next to</u> my knee,
My hand came down <u>on top of</u> him.
But <u>up</u> he flew from me.

Activities: Discuss the meanings of the underlined position words in the poem. Act out the poem, using a toy to place in those positions. Pretend you are a fly and act out its movements.

From *Finger Plays for Home and School,* Copyright © 1990 Scott, Foresman and Company.

Fingers go up

Fingers go up.
Fingers go down.
Fingers go low to the ground.

Fingers go out.
Fingers go in.
Fingers go slowly around.

Activities: Name things that go up in the air and things that are on—or under—the ground. Talk about things that stay IN something and things that stay OUT. Draw things that move slowly and things that move quickly.

I brush my teeth

I brush my teeth
And comb my hair,
Then off to school I go.

I write my name
And do my work,
Then count things in a row.

I eat my lunch
And drink my milk
For these will help me grow.

I read from books
And sing a song,
Then home from school I go.

Activities: How do you get ready for school in the morning? What are your favorite school activities? Draw pictures of things you do in school.

I touch my head

I touch my head.
I touch my toes.
I touch my ears
And then my nose.

I touch my neck.
I touch my hips.
I touch my back
And then my lips.

Activities: Name body parts and tell what they can do. Touch your toes without bending your knees. What foods keep your body healthy?

See my little goldfish

See my little goldfish
Swimming in the sun,
Finds a little minnow—
Make a one.

See my little turtle
Looking up at you,
Moving oh so slowly—
Make a two.

See my little squirrel
Scurry up a tree,
Fluffy tail a-waving—
Make a three.

See my little puppy
Running through the door.
Finds a juicy meat bone—
Make a four.

See my little bunny
Hopping down the drive.
Stops to eat a clover—
Make a five.

See my little rooster
Pecking at the sticks.
Eats a little black bug—
Make a six.

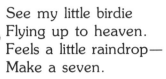
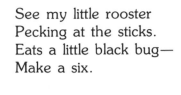

See my little birdie
Flying up to heaven.
Feels a little raindrop—
Make a seven.

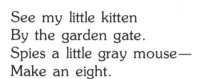

See my little kitten
By the garden gate.
Spies a little gray mouse—
Make an eight.

See my little hamster
On a wheel so fine.
Hops down for some water—
Make a nine.

See my little white hen
Scratching in her pen.
Feeds upon a corn grain—
Make a ten.

Activities: Write the numbers in the air. Count to ten, twenty, etc., to the beat of clapping, nodding, tapping, or hopping. What other words rhyme with the end words?

The great golden dragon

The great golden dragon
Has claws on his toes.
He roars and he rumbles—
Fire pours from his nose.

His great spiny humps
Go way up and go down.
He has teeth, sharp as nails
That you see when he frowns.

His great slashing tail,
Flaps here and flaps there.
He humps and he wriggles—
Scales flash everywhere.

His eyes spark and blaze,
His head swings to the right.
If he looks o'er my way,
I'll run fast out of sight.

Activities: Read about dragons. Act like a dragon. Cut out two identical dragons. Color them. Staple most of the sides together, then stuff the dragon with the leftover scraps. Finish stapling the dragon together.

From *Finger Plays for Home and School,* Copyright © 1990 Scott, Foresman and Company.

Come and see the valentine box

Come and see the valentine box.
It is so tall and wide,
All covered over with red and pink.
Here, have a look inside.

And through the slit, heaped to the top,
Do you see valentines?
Now this is what they all will say:
"Oh, please, will you be mine?"

Activities: Make a valentine box. Cover it with paper and add red and pink hearts. Make animals using hearts for heads, bodies, eyes, legs, etc. Write valentine verses.

I reached up for some paper

I reached up for some paper
And I folded it in half.
I cut a big red heart, then
Wrote a poem to make you laugh.

On back of that red heart,
I made some letters dark and fine,
Then added these dear words,
"Oh, won't you be my valentine?"

Activities: Cut out hearts. With your finger, draw valentine hearts in the air. Talk about Valentine's Day. Find out why we have Valentine's Day.

BE MINE

BE MY VALENTINE

5 little bunnies

5 little bunnies
Go looking for eggs.

4 little bunnies
All hop on their legs.

3 little bunnies
Are twitching their ears.

2 little bunnies
Are drying their tears.

1 little bunny
Cries, "It's Easter Day!"

Then all of the bunnies
Go hopping away.

Activities: Read about rabbits. Act out the finger-play poem. How do you care for pet rabbits?

I woke Easter morning

I woke Easter morning
And hopped to my feet.
I raced to hunt eggs,
Taking no time to eat.

There were eggs under pillows
And eggs behind books.
I found *eggs* inside teapots
And eggs tied to hooks.

But the grandest of all,
In a green grassy nest,
Was a great choc'late egg,
Which I liked super best.

Activities: Draw and color large eggs. Look in the encyclopedia for different kinds of birds' eggs. Which ones have you seen? Why do we celebrate Easter? What animals, other than birds, hatch from eggs?

I have a big fat pumpkin

I have a big fat pumpkin,
Round as he can be.
I scoop out all the little seeds
And carve some eyes to see.

I walk across the squeaky porch
And place him by a tree.
I put in one bright candle light
And watch him smile at me!

Activities: Make pumpkins
from orange paper. Cut a
pumpkin and carve a face.
Read a Halloween story.

I put on my mask

I put on my mask
And I walk down the street.
I knock on the door
And I call, "Trick or Treat!"

I open my sack
And in tumbles a treat.
Then, "Thank you," I call,
As I walk down the street.

Activities: Tell about your Halloween costume or one you would like to have. What do you do on Halloween? Make a picture of you and your friends in your costumes or in costumes you would like to have. Talk about Halloween safety rules.

Thanksgiving Day I look around

Thanksgiving Day I look around,
To see what Mommy makes.
Potatoes, turkey, bread and corn
And pumpkin pies and cakes.

We bow our heads and fold our hands
Before we start to eat.
Say, "Thank You, God, for blessing us
In giving such a treat."

Activities: Draw pictures of the Thanksgiving meal at your home. Why should we thank God for everything? What can you do to help, or to share, at Thanksgiving? Name other things for which you are thankful.

Once all the Pilgrims

Once all the Pilgrims
Put on their warm coats.
They took all their food
And got into a boat.

They put up the sails
And then sailed away.
The strong winds did blow
And they tossed and they swayed.

They shivered with cold,
That brave Pilgrim band,
And after long weeks,
They spotted some land.

They got off the boat
And looked all around.
The Pilgrims cut trees and
Built log homes so sound.

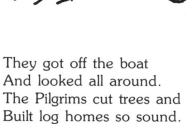

The kind Indians helped them
To plant corn with fish.*
They had a fine harvest,
Sharing food was their wish.

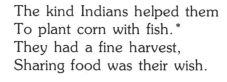

"Thanks," said the Pilgrims,
When the Indians came,
"For helping us all,
We give thanks in God's name."

Activities: Read about the
Pilgrims. Act out the things the
Pilgrims and the Indians did. Make
pictures and put them in order.
(*They planted fish with corn
kernels to help the corn grow.)

From *Finger Plays for Home and School,* Copyright © 1990 Scott, Foresman and Company.

25

We put on our coats

We put on our coats,
Oh! Just hear the wind blow!
With our caps pulled on tight,
We go out in the snow.

We walk toward the woods,
And we search for a tree.
There stands a tall pine,
Just the right one for me.

Daddy swings his strong ax,
The pine falls to the ground.
We tug at the branches,
What a good tree we found!

We both drag it home,
Then we lift it up tall,
Set the trunk in a holder,
Place it next to the wall.

We put on bright lights,
Add some colorful balls.
See the fine Christmas tree?
Come and look, one and all!

Activities: Draw or make Christmas
trees. How can you share at Christmas?
What can you give that cannot be bought
at a store?

From Finger Plays for Home and School, Copyright © 1990 Scott, Foresman and Company.

One little angel

One little angel
With two golden wings
Looked down to the earth
And started to sing.

He saw the small baby,
His eyes fast asleep.
Said the angel so softly,
"My watch I will keep."

He spread out his wings
O'er that small manger bed
And saw the wee baby
Just turning his head.

And then many angels
With eyes shining bright
Saw a star in the sky
On that holiest night.

Activities: Why do we
have Christmas? Christ
child? Stars? Angels? Tell
how you celebrate Christ-
mas. Do you share at
Christmastime? How?

Listen now and you will hear

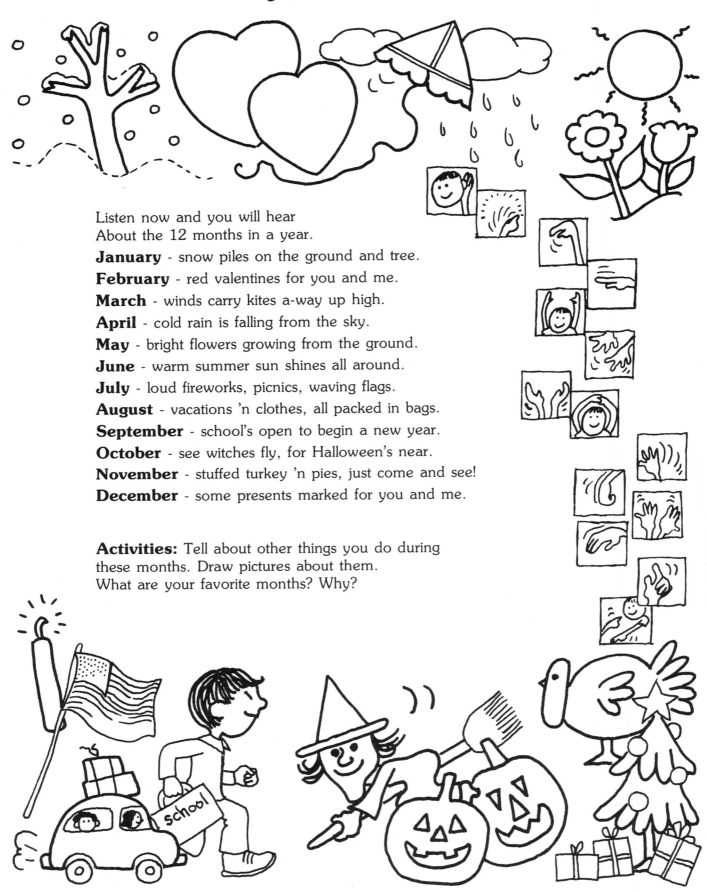

Listen now and you will hear
About the 12 months in a year.

January - snow piles on the ground and tree.

February - red valentines for you and me.

March - winds carry kites a-way up high.

April - cold rain is falling from the sky.

May - bright flowers growing from the ground.

June - warm summer sun shines all around.

July - loud fireworks, picnics, waving flags.

August - vacations 'n clothes, all packed in bags.

September - school's open to begin a new year.

October - see witches fly, for Halloween's near.

November - stuffed turkey 'n pies, just come and see!

December - some presents marked for you and me.

Activities: Tell about other things you do during these months. Draw pictures about them.
What are your favorite months? Why?

Little white snowflakes

Little white snowflakes
Are falling all around.
I will catch them in my hand
Just before they touch the ground.

Little white snowflakes
Are falling on the tree.
They are covering the house
But they won't cover me!

Activities: Pretend you are a snowflake and show what you would do. How can you have fun in the snow? Make snow pictures using cotton for snow.

From *Finger Plays for Home and School*, Copyright © 1990 Scott, Foresman and Company.

I see my little shadow

I see my little shadow,
Standing next to me.
My cat, too, has a shadow,
As does the maple tree.

But then I see the groundhog
Popping from the ground.
He sniffs the air and twitches
And quickly looks around.

If groundhog see his shadow,
Oh, then we all will know
That spring will soon be coming
And gone will be the snow.

Activities: Why do we have shadows?
Why are some long and some short? To
see a shadow, take a flashlight and a toy
into a dark room. Shine the flashlight on
the toy to make a shadow. Draw pictures
of things and their shadows. Go outside
on a sunny day and look for your
shadow. Find shadows of other things.

The cool March winds blow

The cool March winds blow,
And clouds cover the sky.
It's a good day for kites
And for watching them fly.

I take my big kite,
And I lift it up high.
Then I run very fast,
Watch it head for the sky.

I let out the string,
And away goes my kite.
With its long tail a-waving,
I hold the string tight.

My kite dips and turns
In the strong winds on high.
It wiggles and jerks,
As it flies on the sky.

But when the winds cease,
Then my kite stops its mirth.
And so sadly it flutters
Back down to the earth.

Activities: Draw kites.
Pretend you are a kite in the
air and show how you would
act. Fly a kite and watch it.

A little brown seed

A little brown seed
Snug and warm in its bed.
The big yellow sun
Shines so bright overhead.

The rain gently falls.
Can you hear the wind blow?
"Wake up," calls the breeze,
"Little seed, start to grow!"

Activities: What are seeds?
Where do they come from? How
do they grow? What do they need?
Use your body to act out the
poem. Plant seeds and watch them
grow.

32   From *Finger Plays for Home and School*, Copyright © 1990 Scott, Foresman and Company.

The rabbit has some bunnies

The rabbit has some bunnies
In her warm and furry nest.

The cow has one small calf
That runs and doesn't want to rest.

The horse has just one colt
That likes to jump and play and run.

The goat has two small kids
That try to butt and have some fun.

The hen has little chicks
That peck and hunt for bits of corn.

The duck has little goslings
That all follow her each morn.

The sheep has tiny lambs
That run about on dainty feet.

And mother sow has piglets
That all squeal and sleep and eat.

Activities: Make animal booklets.
Talk about animals and their babies.
Make animal sounds.

From *Finger Plays for Home and School,* Copyright © 1990 Scott, Foresman and Company.

33

We all put on our bathing suits

We all put on our bathing suits,
Then to the beach we go.
We take our shovels and our pails,
Find lots of shells to show.

We wade in waves up to our knees,
Splash water way up high.
We build big castles in the sand,
Then watch the sea gulls fly.

Activities: Draw pictures of the poem and put them in order. Act out the poem. Discuss fun things to do in summer.

Leaves are flying

Leaves are flying,
Leaves are flying,
Flying in the breeze.

Leaves are falling,
Leaves are falling,
Falling from the trees.

Try to catch them,
Try to catch them,
Catch them, if you please.

Pile them higher,
Pile them higher,
Higher than your knees.

All jump in them,
All jump in them,
Cover up with leaves.

Activities: Why do leaves fall from trees and how can those leaves be used? What fun things can you do with leaves? Act out a leaf whirling and falling.

The mailman bends to get his mail

The mailman bends to get his mail,
And then he leaves in haste.
He climbs inside his little truck,
For there's no time to waste.

He puts mail into a tray,
Next to him on the seat.
Then when he drives close to our box,
Puts mail inside so neat.

And then he drives on down the street,
Puts mails where it belongs.
I watch him till he's out of sight,
Just moving right along.

Activities: Why do we write and receive letters? Read about mailmen. Do women carry mail to? Write a letter to someone.

U.S. Mail

The firemen hear the clanging bell

The firemen hear the clanging bell,
Put on their coats and boots.
The engine roars, the men hop on
And down the road they scoot!

The sirens blare, the cars all stop
To let the firemen by.
They race ahead and find the fire;
See flames shoot to the sky!

The firemen turn the water on,
Then aim their hoses high.
The people watch the fire die,
Then cheer and wave good-bye.

Activities: Read about firemen. Visit a fire station or ask a fireman to come to your class. Draw pictures of firemen at a fire.

My fingers fly

My fingers fly,
My fingers crawl,
My fingers clap
And then they fall.

My fingers climb,
My fingers leap,
My fingers swim
And then they sleep.

Activities: What things fly, crawl, clap, fall, climb, leap, swim, and sleep? Draw pictures of them and use your body to act out each one of these words. Talk about other words that you can act out.

If I had but one wish

If I had but one wish,
Would I ask for a dish?

No!

Would I ask for a mouse
To live here in our house?

No!

Would I ask for a bear
With soft brown furry hair?

No!

Would I ask for a cat?
To sit here in my hat?

No!

Would I ask for a dragon
I could pull in my wagon?

No!

Would I ask for a train
To go round when it rains?

No!

If I had but one wish,
Would I ask for a fish?

Yes!

Activities: What would
you wish for if you had one
wish? Make a wish book.
What nice things would you
wish for your family?

See the little spider

See the little spider
Climbing on the wall.
She spins a thread of silk
And then she starts to fall.

Sliding down the thread
And dropping to the floor,
Then up she climbs again,
To build her web some more.

When spider's work is done,
She watches with her eyes,
Then sits so very still
And waits to catch some flies.

Activities: Read a book about spiders. Make large, colorful spiders. Search outdoors for spiders and webs. When you find a web, put a piece of heavy paper behind it. Spray the web with hair spray and the web will transfer and stick to the paper.

The train chugs **slowly** up the hill

The train chugs <u>slowly</u> up the hill
And on the railroad track.
Click-ety-clack, click-ety-clack,
Click-ety, click-ety, click-ety, clack.

The train goes <u>faster</u> over the hill
And on the railroad track.
Click-ety-clack, click-ety-clack,
Click-ety, click-ety, click-ety, clack.

The train goes <u>slower</u> into town
And on the railroad track.
Click-ety-clack, click-ety-clack,
Click-ety, click-ety, click-ety, clack.
Woo! Woo!

Activities: Read about trains. Why do we have trains? Act out the finger-play poem, pretending you are the train. Draw pictures of a train, showing the different kinds of cars that make up a train.

I rock baby brother

I rock baby brother
And pat his small head.
I give him his bottle
And put him to bed.

I rock the small cradle
And whisper, "Good night."
Then softly I tiptoe
And turn out the light.

Activities: Instead of the word brother, use sister in the finger-play. Tell about your baby brother or sister—or one you know. Act out actions and sounds babies make. What do babies need?

Finger Puppets

Color the finger puppets. Cut them out. Wrap the puppet bottom around a
finger and cut the tails to overlap slightly. Glue or tape the tails together to fit.

Finger Puppets

From *Finger Plays for Home and School,* Copyright © 1990 Scott, Foresman and Company.